Talking together...

... about contraception

Book One

A practical resource for staff and parents working with young people with learning disabilities

*by Lesley Kerr-Edwards
and Lorna Scott*

Book One is sold as a part of a pack with
**Talking Together ... about contraception
Book Two A book about contraception for
young people with learning disabilities**

fpa

talking sense about sex

Acknowledgements

The authors recognise that this book is based on our work with Image in Action and we would like to thank all the young people and adults with learning disabilities, and staff we have worked with over 19 years who have informed and inspired our work.

Image in Action would like to thank staff and students from the following establishments for their help in trials and consultation on this book:

Acton and West London College, London, Head of Learning Support, Sue Slynn
Furze Down School, Buckinghamshire, Head teacher, Pauline Ditchler
Grapevine, Coventry, Co-ordinator, Manjit Hunja
Oaklands School, Hounslow, Middlesex, Deputy Head teacher, Nicola Christie
Piper Hill School, Manchester, PSHE education Co-ordinator, Linda Otten
Priory School, Suffolk, Teacher, Roger MacKenzie
The Shepherd School, Nottingham, Head teacher, David Stewart
Westbridge Pupil Referral Unit, Ipswich, Teacher, Carey Fish

There have been individuals whose support and comments have been invaluable:

Simon Blake, National Children's Bureau
Claire Fanstone and Toni Belfield, FPA
Rev. Jane Fraser
Jane Nagle, Sarah Duignan and Juliana Slobodian from Image in Action
Simon Needs, Senior Sexual Health Adviser, Middlesex Hospital, Isleworth
Rose O'Connor, Community Nurse, Hammersmith and Fulham Learning Disability Team
Mary Orrell, Community Support Team for people with learning disabilities, The Ridges Learning Centre, Cheshire
Michelle Warne, Teenage Pregnancy Unit, Department for Education and Skills
Pearl Wong, Family Planning Nurse, Emperors Gate Centre for Health, Hammersmith & Fulham
Kim and Cheryl Wyatt

This resource has been commissioned and is supported by the Teenage Pregnancy Unit in the Department for Children, Schools and Families (formerly, Department for Education and Skills), and by the Department of Health.

Talking together ... about contraception
is published by FPA
50 Featherstone Street
London EC1Y 8QU
Tel: 020 7608 5240
Fax: 0845 123 2349
Website: www.fpa.org.uk

British Library Cataloguing in Publication Data. A catalogue record of this book is available from the British Library.

ISBN: 978-1-905506-46-0

Illustrations by Nic Watts © Nic Watts
Designed and typeset by Meg Palmer, Third Column
Printed by Newnorth

This pack can only give you basic information about contraception. The information is based on the evidence-guided research from the World Health Organization and the Faculty of Sexual and Reproductive Healthcare of the Royal College of Obstetricians and Gynaecologists. Different people may give you different information and advice on certain points. All methods of contraception come with a Patient Information Leaflet which provides detailed information about the method.

Remember - contact your doctor, practice nurse or a contraception clinic if you are worried or unsure about anything.

Book One: Contents

Introduction

Why this pack is necessary

People with learning disabilities have the same rights as anyone else to contraceptive information and sexual health services. But they find it harder to exercise those rights. Visiting a clinic to get contraceptive advice can be a daunting experience for anyone, particularly young people. It's far harder for those with learning disabilities.

Contraception is a complex subject and most of the information available is text based and therefore difficult for people with learning disabilities to cope with. They may not have the same discussions with their friends about sex and contraception, yet their need to know about contraceptive choices is just the same.

This pack has been written to provide information at a level that service users can understand and use, using simple language, plenty of visual material and examples of practical activities to promote understanding and skills.

Service users who may be sexually active will need to understand about sexual health and about protecting themselves from sexually transmitted infections (STIs) as well as from unplanned pregnancy. Although some information about STIs is included in these materials, the main focus is on contraception.

For other sexual health resources see *Appendix One* on page 32.

Who this pack is for

This book (Book One) is for parents, carers, teachers, tutors, nurses, youth workers – everyone who works with or supports a person with a learning disability. The accompanying book (Book Two) has been written to be used with groups or individuals with a learning disability, and to be accessible for some of the more able to use on their own. It aims to explain all about contraception, with material for teachers, tutors and others to use in their work or in informal situations, perhaps at home.

Empowerment of people with learning disabilities lies at the heart of these materials. Whatever their race, religion, family background, or the circumstances in which they live, they have the same rights as everyone else to fulfilling sexual relationships if that is what they choose. While these materials largely focus on heterosexual sex, where contraception is most relevant, other relationships are also valued. Everyone has the right to the relationships they choose, and these materials respect a person's sexual orientation, whatever it is. We believe in supporting service users to learn, to understand and to make decisions themselves about their relationships and their sexual behaviour. We also believe in providing conditions in which they can assert and use their independence in every possible way. Understanding about contraception is part of this.

The target group for these materials ranges from service users with severe disabilities to those with mild and moderate disabilities. Some professionals using this pack may not be familiar with people with learning disabilities – their understanding and their behaviour. These service users learn best when work is taken slowly using simple language with plenty of repetition. Their reading skills may not be very good so visual material and uncomplicated pictures work well with them, providing stimulus to help their concentration and to retain what they have been taught. Because of their disability, they may not be allowed as much privacy as other people, and may need extra help to understand the boundaries between public and private. This can show in the behaviours and social skills they may exhibit and the sometimes inappropriate responses they make.

How to use the pack

This pack contains two books.

● *Book One (this book)*

This book is intended for those adults who work with or are involved with the target group of service users: parents, carers, teachers, tutors, nurses, youth workers and other staff.

It provides a guide to the contents of the pack, background information about sexuality and people with learning disabilities, and information on contraception. It also contains separate guides for different services to indicate ways of working with service users and the issues that arise in different circumstances and situations. It suggests some practical activities to help people with learning disabilities learn about contraception and using condoms. The appendices list useful resources, organisations and sources of help. There is also a proforma which you can fill in with local information about opening times of local clinics, bus routes and times, and other relevant details.

● *Book Two*

This accompanying book is intended for use with service users or by service users themselves. Storylines and activities provide opportunities for introducing the subject of contraception and plenty of material for several sessions in a planned programme. The material can also be used in one-to-one situations, to suit the needs of the individual. The need may be for factual information, or it may be to help the service user make appropriate choices about sex and contraception. Information about where and how to access sexual health services may also be required. All these needs are covered in the pack.

Picture posters at the end of the book give simple information about different methods of contraception. The information on the back of each poster is written simply for service users to understand. The contents of this book can be photocopied and used as handouts.

Where to start: pathways through the material

Not everything in this first book is relevant to all services so it's probably a good idea to start by looking at the guide for your particular service to get a feel for which parts may be most useful for you. For instance, you may be working with a group in a sex and relationships education (SRE) programme, with a youth group, talking to a service user in a clinic or general practice, or at home with your son or daughter. Then look at the material in Book Two to consider which parts might be appropriate, and refer to the pathways suggested below.

Examples of pathways through the material in Book Two

- For a group or individual just starting to learn about sexual relationships and making choices then maybe the picture stories on page 50 in Book Two should be the focus.

- If a young woman is speaking one-to-one with a health professional about her unprotected sex then the story about emergency contraception and the picture posters about emergency contraception and condoms are most relevant (see pages 51 and 68 in Book Two).

- If an individual has a lot of sexual relationships and needs some support then the section about where to go for advice and the picture posters are most relevant (see pages 33 and 50 in Book Two). This might also be the place to start with an informed and sexually active group.

- To promote good sexual health, look at the stories about Jack and Maya (see pages 16 and 31 in Book Two). The activity *No Excuses!* on page 29 in this book would also be appropriate.

Some areas of work

1. *Learning the skills of making choices and being assertive*

- Opportunities for making choices can be provided at home and in the classroom.

- Service users can practise assertive statements and think of situations when it is difficult to make decisions.

- Several other resources contain activities and material to support this (see *Appendix One*, page 32).

2. *Understanding sex, contraception and sexual health*

- Find out how much is already known about this.

- Make sure foundation work has taken place, or provide it first.

- Choose one small area of work at a time and develop work around the topic.

- Be aware that understanding about the nature of consent and the consequences of making relationship choices are key areas.

- Refer to other resources.

3. Using the picture stories

- Don't use them all at once. Pick out whichever is most relevant to your situation and needs.

- Read through it slowly with service users or ask them to do so.

- Ask and discuss: what are the characters thinking/feeling? What would be the next step in the story? What difficulties might the characters face and how might they deal with them?

- Use the story as an assessment tool: if the characters wanted to go to a contraception clinic in our area where would that be?

- Discuss the different lifestyles of the characters in the different stories: is this story like anyone we know?

4. Choosing a contraceptive

- Use the picture stories to ask why the characters are making this choice.

- What other choices do people make in relationships, for example, where to go out? Or does the character change clothing if their partner says s/he doesn't like it?

- A teacher or tutor could choose a story of a character which is similar to the students and ask, for example, what would the character think?

- A health professional could personalise the story and ask direct questions, such as, have you told anybody about this or are you going to?

5. Where to go for advice about contraception

- Identify people to talk to, for example, family members.

- Discuss the reliability of advice from friends:

  — What could friends be saying about contraception and sex?

  — What are the myths?

  These statements could be written on cards and the inaccurate ones placed in a bin to show they are wrong.

- Use an activity like Relationship Circles (in *Talking together … about sex and relationships* see *Appendix One*).

- Provide handouts with clear information about a local general practice or contraception clinic.

6. Visiting the general practice or clinic

- Localise the work: Where is your local contraception clinic? What is the phone number? How do you get there?

- Use role play: making a phone call to the clinic or talking to the receptionist.

- Talk about some of the characters in the picture stories and work out what they might need to know when they visit their general practice or contraception clinic: What questions might they need to ask the nurse or the doctor?

- Use these questions to encourage service users to ask their own questions. The teacher or nurse could be in role as the 'expert' to answer the questions.

- Identify who service users can talk to if they have any problems.

7. Some questions people ask ...

- Read the problem first.

- Ask the service users what kind of answers they think are the best ones.

- Now look at what the adviser says and compare the two.

8. Using the picture posters

- Do service users understand the picture sequence?

- Photocopy the pictures, cut them out and ask the service user/s to put them in the right order.

- Ask them what is happening in each picture.

- Use the text on the back to explain the process simply.

- Localise the information: where is our local clinic/pharmacy/doctor?

- Invite a health professional to explain procedure and show actual equipment and contraceptives.

- Photocopy the picture posters so individuals can have their own linformation sheet.

9. Understanding side effects

- Use a person cut out to show where pain is.

- Indicate passage of time by using a calendar.

Your local health promotion service will probably have more visual resources and books if you need them.

Before you start ...

This pack cannot be used in isolation. It's not a good idea to use it unless there has been plenty of prior background work on sexuality. An understanding of body parts and function, the difference between public and private, the skills of permission, choice and negotiation, and how a relationship develops, are all essential.

In whatever context the pack is used, it will be more effective if these conditions can be met:

- try to choose a quiet place and an uninterrupted time

- use the materials a few at a time

- make sure the service user/s understands each part as you go along

- a prearranged visit to a local contraception clinic will help to make service users familiar with the situation and the staff

- support the service user to keep a clinic appointment, and to travel there independently if possible

- make sure the clinic knows the person has a learning disability; they may be able to allow more time for the appointment

- it may be a good idea to take this pack to the clinic

- afterwards, talk about what happened. Does the service user understand what was said? Do they know what to do now?

A note about terminology

The phrase **service user** describes all the different groups of people you can use this pack with – pupils, students, adults.

The word **parents** is used in these materials to include carers, care workers in residential situations and anyone who is in a position of responsibility for the overall care of the service user.

Contraception clinics are sometimes known as sexual health clinics or family planning clinics. They offer free contraception, pregnancy testing and some tests and treatment for STIs. They may also offer sessions specifically for young people.

General practice is used to refer to the team that includes doctors and practice nurses.

About sexuality and people with learning disabilities

Sexuality and people with learning disabilities

Sex is for everyone, if they choose, regardless of sexual orientation. People with learning disabilities have the same rights, feelings and needs as everyone else. Their physical development is generally no different. What may be different is the availability of information which they can understand and make use of, and the amount of support they may need to undertake and sustain a loving sexual relationship.

Their learning is likely to be slower, which is why we need to start talking about sex and relationships as early as possible. Parents can make use of family situations, a relative having a baby, for instance, or TV programmes, to help their child understand what's happening. This needs to go on all the time, to remind and reinforce the learning. In school, it's no good expecting a programme which starts at age 16 to provide sufficient time for young people to do the basic work on physical development as well as getting to the vital material on sexual relationships, safer sex and contraception.

Service users are most likely to be carefully informed and supported when everyone plays a part: the home, the school, the college, the general practice or contraception clinic. It is at home that the family's values, culture and any religious views are passed on to the children, and where the most effective loving support is usually found. Schools have a key role, using methods which help young people to understand the necessary knowledge and which enable them to gain and practise the relevant personal skills. In a health setting (and often in the classroom too), health professionals have the sensitive job of explaining in simple terms the way contraception works, and helping people to decide the best choice for themselves. Their task will be all the harder if the service user has missed out on early learning elsewhere.

Activities described in this pack will be suitable for all these situations, but nothing will take the place of all parties working together for the greatest benefit to the service users. These materials present a range of situations and relationships in which contraception and sexual health are an issue, so that they may be useful to as many people as possible. Depending on our own views, or the moral framework expressed in a school policy for example, we may choose to use some scenarios rather than others. There is no definitive position held here, except that sexual encounters should ideally take place within a loving and respectful relationship which values both partners.

Whatever the context, there are some key things to think about when we are preparing to do work on contraception. Do the service users have sufficient understanding of body parts and functions? Have they had an opportunity to consider a range of relationships and the issues involved in beginning a sexual relationship? Have we all agreed an acceptable language for genitals and sexual activity? Anyone learning about sexual relationships needs to be made aware of the possibility of coming into contact with STIs, including HIV. Is this included in the programme? Some of this work will take place in schools, but everyone involved will need to think about the values, which are explicit or implicit in the programme and about partnership and marriage, for instance, and about same sex partnerships.

A school or other establishment will have made sure that their policy covers these matters, so that there is broad agreement among the school community for a consistent message to be given. Parents and carers may feel anxious or embarrassed about raising these issues, and may welcome support to talk about these matters at home. But we mustn't assume that teachers, tutors and other staff find it easy to talk about sex and sexuality and some prior training may be necessary. Here, health professionals may have a clear role within the partnership, to impart their specialist knowledge to others. Schools will contribute their experience of suitable methods and activities, while parents and carers will have the intimate understanding of the needs and abilities of their children.

Among other things, this pack is dedicated to the idea of partnership. Time taken to work together is never wasted. Plenty of communication and consultation with all interested parties is essential. As parents, teachers, tutors or health staff, we all have views about contraception, maybe religious, maybe cultural, and these views must be taken into account.

Talking about contraception involves acknowledging that there are feelings engaged, as well as knowledge of facts. Above all, we must all allow plenty of time and use a variety of activities so that service users can understand and absorb the important messages we are trying to give.

What follows are suggestions for different users of the pack: schools and colleges, parents and carers, health staff and youth workers. But there are others who may find the material useful. Day or residential centre staff may find themselves accompanying a person to the general practice or a contraception clinic, for example, or having to make sure that contraceptives are taken regularly. Sometimes voluntary organisations may become involved. It's important that everyone who may have some part to play has an understanding of service users' needs and how to meet them, matters which this pack explores and explains. And equally essential is that everyone involved works together to give and get the best service for these vulnerable people, for whom consistency and security are vital.

Specially for schools and colleges ...

There is more to SRE than just learning about sexuality. In schools there is much groundwork to be done on growing up, puberty, body parts, gender, public and private, and appropriate behaviour. Learning and practising skills will be an integral part throughout the programme so that students will develop their ability to choose for themselves, to make decisions and to assert themselves, all in a range of different situations. Practise and using active methods helps to 'fix' the learning experience. For learning involves more than 'knowing what' – the facts. It also requires 'knowing how' – the skills.

When we talk about sex we are working with personal matters: bodies, relationships, feelings and sexuality. To this we all bring our own experiences and opinions. This means taking a lot of care so that these views are acknowledged and service users' experiences contained in a safe manner. In the classroom, some elements of safe work are:

● creating clear ground rules and lines of referral

● observing confidentiality: it's a good idea to make sure your establishment has a policy on confidentiality in place to support SRE work

- using 'distancing' methods, which focus on other people: these include case studies, role play and stories, so that we talk about 'her', 'him', 'them', rather than 'you', 'me' and 'us'.

School and college programmes need to be carefully planned, consistent and thorough, providing a coherent experience from an early age. A well designed course will offer a variety of elements — some for groups, some to meet individual needs. One-to-one support is offered in some places, and the school nurse often makes a valuable contribution as a member of the personal, social, health and economics education (PSHE) team. Governors clearly have a key role here and the support given by learning support assistants (LSAs) can be crucial. It's not only the programme that needs to be consistent. Working in the same space which offers privacy, with the same staff and the same group members is important too. This all helps group members feel secure and speeds learning.

It's often schools which take the initiative in approaching and working with parents and carers to make sure they are consulted about their children's needs and their family's values. Parents want to know what the school is teaching, and when, so that they have an opportunity to talk about it at the right moment at home. These materials offer ideas for things that parents can do with their young people, and there are some other excellent resources which you can suggest they use.

On the following pages, we offer some examples of SRE programmes suitable for different age and ability groups to support the planning process. The following are taken from Image in Action's book, *Let's plan it*.

- a curriculum plan for primary school pupils with learning disabilities

- a plan for secondary school pupils with severe learning disabilities

- a range of topics for older students with mild and moderate learning disabilities.

A plan for primary school pupils with learning disabilities

RECEPTION – YEAR THREE Age 4–8 years

Learning to be in a group – circle work, naming, turn taking.

Basic social skills, for example, eye contact.

Themes

1 **Body parts:** recognition of own body parts, for example, hands, feet, using songs or painting.

2 **Recognition of self:** for example, as own gender.

3 **Public and private:** staff acknowledgement of private places, such as toilets and private body parts.

4 **Feelings:** named, acknowledged and valued by staff.

5 **Relationships:** recognition that there is self and there are others; valuing positive behaviour; beginnings of friendships; recognising differences, such as hair colour.

6 **Life cycle:** recognising family relationships, and that these are different from relationships at school.

YEARS FOUR to FIVE Age 8–10 years

Development of group through circle activities – trust games, turn taking.

Skills: assertion, permission, decision making – early stages.

Themes

1 **Body parts:** naming all body parts.

2 **Gender:** boy/girl, man/woman; recognition of gender of others.

3 **Public and private:** use of toilets; where is a private place at home?

4 **Feelings:** recognising and naming own feelings, and that they can have an effect on others.

5 **Relationships:** appropriate touch; friends; co-operation in groups.

6 **Life cycle:** difference between themselves as children and as babies.

YEAR SIX Age 10–11 years

*Identity of group: ownership – it's **their** space.*

Understanding that the session is private.

Making choices about activities and leading some activities.

Creating own ground rules.

Skills: assertion work – implications of saying yes and no, developing real choices students make in and out of school.

Themes

1 **Body parts:** naming public and private body parts; understanding body function; menstruation.

2 **Gender:** physical differences between male and female.

3 **Public and private:** examples of private places; gender distinctions relating to privacy.

4 **Feelings:** self and others; extend range of feelings recognised.

5 **Relationships:** in and outside school; family, friends, strangers.

6 **Life cycle:** place in life cycle, for example, baby, child, teenager, adult; introducing body changes and puberty.

A plan for secondary school pupils with severe learning disabilities

Themes from the primary years are reinforced and developed in the secondary phase. Often this means repeating earlier work to provide a basis for the more explicit work in the later years.

KEY STAGE THREE – YEARS SEVEN to NINE Age 11–14 years

Activities to consolidate group development, especially if this is a new group: circle work, naming, turn taking.

Continuation of themes in year six, reinforced and extended.

Themes

1 **Body parts:** naming public and private body parts; body function, menstruation and masturbation.

2 **Gender:** physical differences between male and female.

3 **Public and private:** privacy required for masturbation; developing own rights to privacy.

4 **Feelings:** consequences of feelings; changes in feelings, and including sexual feelings.

5 **Relationships:** importance of peer group, and students relating to one another; strategies for forming friendships; pairing and 'special friends'.

6 **Life cycle:** body changes and puberty; growing and changing.

KEY STAGE FOUR – YEARS TEN and ELEVEN Age 14–16 years

Continue reinforcement of group identity.

Emphasis on decision making, assertion and negotiation skills, and transferring knowledge outside school.

Offering more opportunities for independent choices and action.

Developing work on sexual relationships and feelings.

Themes

1 **Body parts:** sexual body parts; similarities and differences between the sexes; physical abilities and disabilities; awareness of race.

2 **Gender:** recognising stereotypes.

3 **Public and private:** creating privacy; transferring concept to other situations; appropriate behaviour; developing own rights to privacy (in bathroom, bedroom, and with property).

4 **Feelings:** recognising body language; response to situations; managing feelings; sexual feelings; understanding 'fancying' and 'feeling sexy'.

5 **Relationships:** special friendships; development of sexual relationships; practising relationship skills; introducing safer sex and contraception.

6 **Life cycle:** sexual body changes; changes in status and relationships.

OLDER STUDENTS Aged 16–19 years

Much of the material covered will repeat and reinforce earlier learning. This is where the particular needs and abilities of the students will influence choice and development of topics.

Themes

1 **Body parts:** sexual function of body parts; information on availability of support for sexual activity if physical disability makes it difficult.

2 **Gender:** challenging stereotypes; race and gender; roles in parenting.

3 **Public and private:** understanding others' need for privacy; privacy for an intimate relationship; and confidentiality.

4 **Feelings:** sexual feelings; desire and sexual response; awareness of own and others' sexual feelings.

5 **Relationships:** developing an intimate relationship; awareness of the range of sexual relationships; sexual health; safer sex and HIV; negotiating a relationship.

6 **Life cycle:** contraception; conception, pregnancy, birth; parenting and child rearing; sources of support.

A range of topics for older students with moderate learning disabilities

Below is a range of possible topics which students with moderate learning disability (MLD) may want and need to cover as a part of a sex and relationships programme. The list is not exhaustive as each group will have different needs and priorities. The topics are listed in a possible sequence to use with a group. They build on basic skills, then cover factual and biological knowledge before moving on to more complex skills and issues.

- **Types of relationship**.
- **Stereotypes** – dealing with media and peer pressure – for example, gender, sexuality, age and experience.
- **Assertion skills** – saying 'no' and resisting pressure.
- **Biological knowledge** – body parts, functions and fluids.
- **Vocabulary** – body parts, sexual activity.
- **The law** – age of consent, homosexuality, consent issues, confidentiality.
- **Parental attitudes and conflicts**.
- **Dating** – appropriate touch, trust, consent and personal safety.
- **Sequence of events in relationships**.
- **Sex, choice and decision making** – resisting pressure, reasons for having sex.
- **Contraceptive choices**.
- **STIs and HIV**.
- **Safer sex and condom use**.

- **Local services and what happens at contraception and sexual health clinics**.

- **Negotiating safer sex** – assertion and non-penetrative activity.

- **Choice and positive image of different types of relationships** – for example, gay and lesbian relationships, being single, and cultural differences.

- **Myths** – dispelling myths about sex, contraception and infections.

Work on group building, assertion, self-esteem, choice and decision making needs to run parallel with work on these topics.

Specially for parents and carers …

Adolescence is a particularly challenging time for parents of a son or daughter with a learning disability. We watch their developing sexuality and maturity with mixed feelings; glad that they are growing up but anxious about what these developments may bring. We want the best for our child, with a secure future in good hands. Some parents may secretly hope that their child will never become interested in sex, with the potential complications it may bring. Others can become so anxious about the vulnerability of their child that he or she is never allowed any independent life.

It's right to want to help our young people to avoid being exploited or hurt – that's common to all parents. What we must remember is that ignorance never protects. There are well established ways of teaching young people with learning disabilities the essential information they need about sex; and proven methods of helping them to learn the skills they need to manage all their relationships successfully: how to greet and behave appropriately with different people; how to make choices; how to assert themselves so that they can avoid difficult situations. And part of that necessary learning is about how to protect themselves in sexual situations.

This may not be relevant for a few of our young people, but many adults with learning disabilities can enjoy a satisfying sexual partnership which enhances many aspects of their lives. For their protection they will need to understand about avoiding unplanned pregnancies, and avoiding STIs. Because they learn more slowly than others, it's essential that learning about sex and relationships begins early. Schools can introduce the basic knowledge about how bodies work and grow as soon as children enter school; and a good school programme will carry on throughout the years until they leave. But the learning will be faster and longer lasting if it is shared with the adults at home, so that everyone has the same approach, each reinforcing what the other is doing.

A good school will take care to involve its parents in all this, consulting them and letting them know what's being taught. As parents we can take an active part in this partnership. It's a good idea to discuss with the school about the words that are to be used by everyone, and the visual and other materials they use. Perhaps ask them to let parents know what they are doing in a regular newsletter. Some schools run workshops for parents so that they can talk about their views and their anxieties. Schools can often suggest books and other materials that parents can use at home; some schools have a lending system for this. It's worth making enquiries.

There are other sources of help available to parents. Perhaps most reassuring are the other parents we meet in informal networks and social gatherings, who have similar experiences to our own. There are a number of voluntary organisations, sometimes with a local group, which can offer support. You can find details at the local library, or from school or college.

If the time comes when a young person needs specific advice about contraception, the first person to talk to about this may be your doctor or practice nurse. Or you and your child may prefer to go to a contraception clinic or young people's service, to see specialist staff. You may wish to accompany your child, or another adult may do so, but for a young adult who has a relationship with a partner, it is probably more appropriate if they visit the clinic together, where trained health professionals should be able to help them to make the best decisions. Clients can ask for a longer appointment time at the clinic.

You may find the picture posters on contraceptives in Book Two in this pack useful. You could read them with your son or daughter if they can't manage to do so on their own. It's a good idea to introduce them to condoms by getting some that they can open and examine. Condoms can help protect against most infections that can be caught through sexual contact, like HIV, chlamydia and gonorrhoea.

Specially for health professionals …

Most clients who attend contraception or sexual health services or a general practice do not have learning disabilities, and staff may be unfamiliar with the best way to communicate with those who do. These service users may have few literacy skills so visual material will work best with them. They will probably need more time for a consultation than more able people, and will benefit from a follow up appointment. A reminder of the date may also be a good idea.

It's possible that another adult will accompany the service user. If so, it's important to try to avoid talking 'through' the supporting adult; one of your tasks will be to find out what the service user's own wants and needs are. Current good practice is to be inclusive and to help the client make their own decisions. The supporter can be of great help. As they know the individual, they may be able to guide you about what kind of information the service user needs, and in what format. You could ask them to help you pitch the information at the correct level. It may be necessary to keep in touch with parents or carers who can support the service users in their choices – and their memory – though people with learning disabilities have the same rights to confidentiality as anyone else. In this work we all need to form strong partnerships – health workers, parents, carers, school and college staff – if we are to be effective in helping the service user.

It may be necessary to simplify the language and terms used. For instance there may be no need to name the hormones or to talk about fallopian tubes. Try to use short clear sentences. We recommend using correct terms for body parts but it may be useful to check out the service user's comprehension and use common slang terms to back up your point. You might say, for example, "The condom goes on the man's penis. You may know it as a willy". Some people with learning disabilities may appear to understand and may fear being ridiculed or losing face if they appear not to understand. You may need to find several different ways to repeat the same point, perhaps with a leaflet, a picture, then a 3D resource. Someone with a learning disability may not be able to take in a lot of information at once and may benefit from several sessions and repetitions.

A collection of resources will be useful to aid communication. In this one-to-one format some simple basic information may need to be transmitted. If the service user hasn't received much tuition about their body and how its works, the job of the health professional will be made more difficult. 3D resources, such as penis models and models of female genitalia, are very useful. The scenarios and stories in Book Two of this pack can be used to discuss the most suitable method of contraception for the client. The picture posters are designed to provide simple information about each method, and could be read together.

One of the most effective ways of helping people with learning disabilities understand contraception is to work in partnership with local schools, colleges or centres. Some pilot schemes have worked well where a health professional visits a group of service users as part of their SRE programme. After previous work carefully planned by the teacher or tutor, the service users get to know the doctor or nurse and can get the information they need in an informal context. Then they visit the clinic to be introduced to what happens there. These pilots have found that service users gain both information and confidence from the experience, and are more likely to feel that the clinic is accessible to them if they need it.

Specially for youth service workers ...

Young people with learning disabilities may be found in the youth service in many different contexts, sometimes in segregated sessions, but also taking part in the wide range of services and activities offered to young people as a whole.

These young people are not always readily identifiable in non-segregated groups, presenting a wide variety of abilities, skills and understanding. Some may appear streetwise, especially those with moderate disabilities, but their comprehension may not concur with the image they present. These young people may be more vulnerable to exploitation than others of their age group, especially as they can sometimes display affection to those who show an interest in them.

All this means that they need a good deal of help if they are to form and enjoy safe and satisfying sexual relationships. Understanding the complexities of making choices about contraception and accessing services may prove particularly problematic.

Informal services can create a flexible and relaxed environment in which young people can talk about issues of a sexual nature; and they can complement the more formal SRE programmes offered in schools and colleges. In these conditions, youth service workers can respond to personal requests from young people who ask for information and advice about pregnancy, condom use, contraceptive methods, and when they have had unprotected sex.

Opportunities offer themselves for work at several levels: through planned one-to-one work, individual crisis support, on an informal ad hoc basis, within planned programmes, in group work, and during media, arts and sports events. Young people with learning disabilities may need help to be aware of what can be on offer and need additional time to work through the themes so that they can understand their relevance to their own situation. Some young people may prefer working in single sex groups according to their wishes and cultural needs and values.

What works best are active methods and relevant resources that enable young people to participate and say what they want to learn. Role play and drama activities are enjoyed; they enrich and enhance learning, as well as providing opportunities to develop and practise skills.

It goes without saying that sex and relationships work should always be backed up with relevant policies and establishment guidelines, including definition of boundaries and appreciation of confidentiality issues. The combination of sensitive material and vulnerable young people demands careful approaches and support for the practitioners. But with these in place, some exciting and valuable work can take place.

Working in partnership can be the key to responding well. There are a multiplicity of people and organisations that are involved in the care of these young people, and in supporting their right as sexual beings to information about sexuality. Among these are health professionals who may be involved in providing contraceptive advice and services, and who can be invited into youth service sessions to work with young people. And although not obliged to inform parents, it's good practice to consider the benefits of working in partnership with parents on sex and relationships issues. We're all in this together to help some of the most vulnerable young people in our society.

Guide to contraception

The picture posters in the accompanying Book Two describe the methods of contraception which we have been told are the ones most frequently used by people with learning disabilities because they are the easiest to use, although practice may vary from place to place.

Each picture poster tells the story of people who are using them and gives some basic information about the contraceptive on the back. They have been written very simply, either for use with individuals or groups, or for some service users to read on their own. Professionals and other adults who are using the material in Book Two with people with learning disabilities should refer to the guide on these pages for full information about the different methods of contraception and their effects.

The following section in this book provides more information on all the effective methods of contraception available, which may be helpful for those of us who are not health professionals. This book can only give basic information and as research is ongoing information does change. You can contact the FPA helpline or visit www.fpa.org.uk to check on any points and ensure that your information is up-to-date. FPA has a range of booklets which provides more detailed information on individual methods. (*See Appendix One, page 32.*)

Where to get contraception

Contraception is free for men and women of **all** ages through the National Health Service.

- You can find out about all sexual health services from **sexual health direct**, run by FPA, on 0845 122 8690 or at www.fpa.org.uk.

- You can find details of general practices and pharmacies in England at www.nhs.uk and in Wales at www.wales.nhs.uk. In Scotland you can find details of general practices at www.show.scot.nhs.uk. In England and Wales you can also call NHS Direct on 0845 46 47 and in Scotland NHS 24 on 0845 4 24 24 24. In Northern Ireland call the FPA helpline on 0845 122 8687 or for details of general practices see www.n-i.nhs.uk.

- You can also get details of your nearest contraception, genitourinary medicine (GUM) or sexual health clinic from a telephone directory, health centre, local pharmacy, hospital, midwife, health visitor or advice centre.

- You can get details of young people's services from Brook on 0808 802 1234, www.brook.org.uk or from Sexwise on 0800 28 29 30.

Methods of contraception

Methods with no user failure

These are methods which do not rely on the user remembering to take or use contraception. They are highly effective, but do not offer protection against STIs.

Some methods, particularly those using hormones, may not be suitable for all women and must be discussed with a health professional.

Contraceptive injections

(OVER 99% EFFECTIVE)

Releases the hormone progestogen into the body. This mainly works by stopping ovulation (when the ovaries release an egg), it also thickens cervical mucus to make it difficult for sperm to reach an egg and thins the lining of the uterus (womb) to prevent a fertilised egg implanting. There are two types of injection, Depo-Provera which lasts for 12 weeks and Noristerat which lasts for eight weeks.

Advantages

— Don't have to think about contraception for as long as the injection lasts.
— Doesn't interrupt sex.
— May give some protection against cancer of the uterus and offers some protection from pelvic inflammatory disease.
— The injections are not affected by other medicines.

Disadvantages

— Periods may change in a way that is not acceptable to you.
— Periods and fertility may take time to return to normal after stopping the Depo-Provera injection.
— Women may put on weight when they use Depo-Provera.
— Possible temporary side effects include acne and breast tenderness.
— Can't be removed from the body, so if women have any side-effects they have to be prepared for them to continue during this time, and for some time afterwards.
— Some women are scared of needles.

Contraceptive implant

(**OVER 99% EFFECTIVE**)

Small flexible rod inserted under the skin of your upper arm. It needs to be inserted by a trained doctor or nurse, who will use a local anaesthetic. The main way it works is to stop the ovaries releasing an egg each month (ovulation). It also thickens the mucus from the cervix. This makes it difficult for sperm to move through it and reach an egg. It also makes the lining of the uterus thinner so it is less likely to accept a fertilised egg. It works for three years.

Advantages

— Don't have to think about contraception for as long as the implant is in place.

— Doesn't interrupt sex.

— Fertility returns to normal when the implant is removed.

— It works for three years but can be taken out sooner.

Disadvantages

— Periods may change in a way that is not acceptable to you.

— Other possible temporary side effects include acne and breast tenderness.

— Some medicines may make an implant less effective.

— The implant can be felt under the skin – some women with learning disabilities may pick at it or forget why it is there and worry.

— The implant requires a small procedure to insert and remove it.

The IUS (Intrauterine system)

(**OVER 99% EFFECTIVE**)

A small T-shaped plastic device which releases a progestogen hormone is put into the uterus. This thickens cervical mucus to make it difficult for sperm to reach an egg, thins the lining of the uterus to prevent a fertilised egg implanting and may stop the ovary releasing an egg (ovulation). It works for five years but can be taken out at any time.

Advantages

— Doesn't interrupt sex.

— Periods will usually be much lighter, shorter and sometimes less painful.
They may stop altogether after the first year of use.

— Fertility will return to normal when the IUS is removed.

— It is not affected by any other medicines.

Disadvantages

— Irregular bleeding or spotting is common in the first six months.

— May be temporary side effects such as headaches, acne and breast tenderness.

— Very small chance of getting an infection during the first 20 days after insertion.

— Small increased risk of ectopic pregnancy (where a pregnancy develops outside the uterus, usually in a fallopian tube) if the method fails.

— The IUS can be pushed out by the uterus (expulsion) or it can move (displacement). This is not common. Women fitted with an IUS will be taught how to check their IUS threads every month.

The IUD (Intrauterine device)

(AROUND 99% EFFECTIVE)

A small plastic and copper device is put into the uterus by a trained doctor or nurse. It stops sperm meeting an egg or may stop a fertilised egg implanting in the uterus. It can stay in for 5–10 years depending on type, but can be taken out at any time.

Advantages

— It doesn't interrupt sex.

— Fertility will return to normal when it is removed.

— It works as soon as it is put in.

Disadvantages

— May not be suitable for women at risk of getting an STI.

— Periods may be heavier or longer and more painful. This may improve after a few months.

— Very small chance of getting an infection during the first 20 days after insertion.

— Small increased risk of ectopic pregnancy (where a pregnancy develops outside the uterus, usually in a fallopian tube) if the method fails.

— The IUD can be pushed out by the uterus (expulsion) or it can move (displacement). Women fitted with an IUD will be taught how to check their IUD threads every month.

Male and female sterilisation

These are permanent methods of contraception, which are not usually advised for young people, so we have not included details in this pack. Counselling is important before sterilisation can take place.

Methods with user failure

These methods rely on the user thinking about them regularly or each time they have sex. To be effective, they must be used according to instructions.

The contraceptive patch

(OVER 99% EFFECTIVE, IF USED ACCORDING TO INSTRUCTIONS)

A small patch is stuck on the skin which releases two hormones — estrogen and progestogen. It stops ovulation, thickens cervical mucus to prevent sperm reaching an egg and thins the lining of the uterus to prevent a fertilised egg implanting. A new patch is applied each week for three weeks, followed by one patch-free week when a bleed will occur.

Advantages

— Doesn't interrupt sex.

— Can make bleeds regular, lighter and less painful.

— It is not affected if you have diarrhoea or vomit.

— Fertility returns to normal when patch is no longer used.

Disadvantages

— Very low risk but serious side effects which include blood clots (thrombosis), breast cancer and cervical cancer.

— Can be temporary minor side effects such as headaches, nausea, breast tenderness and mood changes.

— Possible skin irritation where patch is stuck to the skin.

— It can be seen.

— Some medicines may make it less effective.

— It may increase blood pressure.

Contraceptive vaginal ring

(**OVER 99% EFFECTIVE IF USED ACCORDING TO INSTRUCTIONS**)

A small, flexible, plastic ring put into the vagina releases estrogen and progestogen. This stops ovulation, thickens cervical mucus to prevent sperm reaching an egg, and thins the lining of the uterus to prevent a fertilised egg implanting.

Advantages

— Don't have to think about it every day.

— Not affected by vomiting or diarrhoea.

— Can make bleeds regular, lighter and less painful.

— May protect against cancer of the ovary, colon and uterus.

— Fertility returns to normal when use is stopped.

Disadvantages

— Very low risk but serious side effects may include blood clots, breast and cervical cancer.

— Can be temporary side effects including increased vaginal discharge, headaches, nausea, breast tenderness and mood changes.

— Women must be comfortable inserting and removing it.

— Some medicines make it less effective.

— Breakthrough bleeding and spotting may occur in the first few months.

The combined pill

OVER 99% EFFECTIVE IF TAKEN ACCORDING TO INSTRUCTIONS

There are different types of combined pill. Some are taken each day for 21 days, followed by seven pill-free days. Others (Everyday pills) are packs containing 21 active pills and seven inactive ones, so a pill is taken every day without a break.

The pill contains two hormones, estrogen and progestogen. It stops the ovaries from releasing an egg (ovulation), thickens cervical mucus to prevent sperm reaching an egg and thins the lining of the uterus to prevent a fertilised egg implanting.

Advantages

— Doesn't interrupt sex.

— Usually makes bleeds regular, lighter and less painful.

— Reduces the risk of cancer of the ovary, uterus and colon and may protect against pelvic inflammatory disease.

— Fertility returns to normal when the pill is stopped.

Disadvantages

— Very low risk but serious side effects may include blood clots (thrombosis), breast cancer and cervical cancer.

— Can be temporary minor side effects such as headaches, nausea, mood changes and tender breasts.

— Some medicines, vomiting or severe, long-lasting diarrhoea can make it less effective.

— Some women may forget to take it every day.

The progestogen-only pill

99% EFFECTIVE IF TAKEN ACCORDING TO INSTRUCTIONS

A pill containing a progestogen hormone is taken at the same time every day. It thickens cervical mucus to prevent sperm reaching an egg and thins the lining of the uterus to prevent a fertilised egg implanting. In some women it stops the ovaries releasing an egg (ovulation).

Advantages

— Doesn't interrupt sex.

— No serious side effects.

— Can be used by women who cannot use estrogen.

— Fertility returns to normal when the pill is stopped.

Disadvantages

— Periods may change in a way that is not acceptable to you.

— Some temporary side effects such as acne, breast tenderness, weight gain and headaches.

— Some women may forget to take it at the same time every day – most progestogen-only pills can only be taken up to three hours late to be effective. However, there is one type of pill which gives women a slightly longer time to take it in, if it is missed.

The male condom

(98% EFFECTIVE IF USED ACCORDING TO INSTRUCTIONS)

The condom is made of very thin latex (rubber) or polyurethane (plastic) and is put over a man's erect penis before it touches the genital area. It stops sperm from entering a woman's vagina and meeting an egg.

Advantages

— Only needs to be used when having sex.

— Widely available and a variety of types to choose from.

— Helps to protect both partners from some STIs, including HIV.

— No side effects.

Disadvantages

— Putting it on can interrupt sex.

— May slip off or split if not used correctly.

— Man has to withdraw as soon as he has ejaculated and be careful not to spill any semen.

— There are some novelty condoms which are designed purely for fun and should not be used for contraception – it will say so on the packet.

— Oil based lubricants damage latex condoms, but can be used with polyurethane condoms.

— Needs a degree of co-ordination and skill to be put on and taken off properly.

The female condom

(95% EFFECTIVE IF USED ACCORDING TO INSTRUCTIONS)

A soft polyurethane (plastic) sheath loosely lines the vagina. It stops sperm entering the vagina and meeting an egg.

Advantages

— Can be put in any time before sex.

— Helps to protect both partners from some STIs, including HIV.

— No side effects.

— Can be used with any kind of lubricant.

Disadvantages

— Putting it in can interrupt sex (though it can be put in anytime beforehand).

— Need to make sure the man's penis enters the condom and not between the vagina and the condom.

— May get pushed too far into the vagina, which makes it less effective.

— Expensive to buy and more difficult to find than male condoms.

— Needs a degree of co-ordination and skill to be put in.

Diaphragm/cap with spermicide

(92–96% EFFECTIVE IF USED ACCORDING TO INSTRUCTIONS)

A flexible latex (rubber) or silicone device, used with spermicide, is put into the vagina to cover the cervix. This stops sperm from entering the uterus and meeting an egg.

Advantages

— Can be put in any time before sex.

— May protect against cancer of the cervix.

— There are a variety of types to choose from.

— No serious health risks.

Disadvantages

— Putting it in can interrupt sex.

— Some people find the spermicide messy and may be sensitive to the chemical in it.

— Cystitis can be a problem for some diaphragm users.

— It can take time to learn how to use correctly.

— Putting it in needs a degree of skill and co-ordination.

Natural family planning

(UP TO 99% EFFECTIVE IF USED ACCORDING TO INSTRUCTIONS)

The fertile and infertile times of the menstrual cycle are identified by noting the different fertility indicators. Using several indicators, this method is 99% effective, but it needs to be learnt from a trained natural family planning teacher and takes time to learn. Instructions and teaching then need to be followed carefully and sex avoided (or a condom used) at the fertile times of a woman's menstrual cycle. It also requires co-operation from a partner to use this method. It may therefore, not be a first choice method for women with learning disabilities.

Emergency contraception

There are two methods which can be used if a woman has sex without contraception, or if she thinks her method has failed — a hormonal method and a copper IUD.

Hormonal emergency contraception/emergency contraceptive pill

The emergency contraceptive pill contains a progestogen hormone and comes as a single pill. It can be used within three days (72 hours) of unprotected sex. It is more effective the sooner it is taken after unprotected sex. It works by stopping or delaying ovulation or stopping a fertilised egg from implanting in the uterus:

— If taken within 24 hours it will prevent up to 95 per cent of pregnancies that would have occurred if no emergency contraception had been used.

— If taken 72 hours after unprotected sex it will prevent up to 58 per cent of pregnancies that would have occurred if no emergency contraception had been used.

Hormonal emergency contraception is available free from any general practice that provides contraceptive services, contraception clinics, a young people's service, a sexual health clinic, some genitourinary (GUM) clinics, most NHS walk-in centres (in England only), many pharmacies, and some accident and emergency departments. Women aged 16 and over can also buy it from most pharmacies and some privately run clinics.

It is not as effective as using other contraceptive methods regularly, but can be used more than once.

The emergency IUD

This can be inserted into the uterus up to five days after unprotected sex, or up to five days after the earliest time a woman could have released an egg (ovulated). The IUD may stop an egg being fertilised or implanting in the uterus. As well as providing emergency contraception, it can provide long term contraception.

The emergency IUD is the most effective method of emergency contraception. It will prevent up to 99 per cent of pregnancies that would have occurred if no emergency contraception had been used.

See information about IUDs on page 22.

Some useful activities

This section contains a sample of some of the activities that can be used in the classroom, at home or in the clinic. Other activities can be found in *Let's Do It, Let's Plan It* and *Talking together ... about sex and relationships* (details in *Appendix One*).

What goes where?

> **Purpose:** understanding which contraceptive goes with which part of the body.
>
> **Previous knowledge:** service users need to have an understanding of body parts and privacy.

How to do it:

- Use a picture of a woman with no clothes on.

- Photocopy pictures of different contraceptives. Health professionals may wish to use real contraceptives. (Non-health professionals are not allowed to use prescription-only products.) For schools, FPA sells the *Contraceptive display kit*, which contains laminate pill cards, an empty pill box, male and female condoms, and placebos of the other methods of contraception.

STAGE ONE: Identifying the contraceptives

- Lay out the contraceptives/contraceptive pictures. Ask the service user to match them one by one to parts of the woman's body, listening to the names s/he uses and reminding them of the correct names.

- Once they are matched ask how the contraceptives get into a woman's body, for example the pill by mouth, the injection with a needle under the skin, the IUD/IUS by insertion into the uterus through the vagina.

- To aid understanding, other objects could be compared such as a vitamin pill, earring or tampon.

STAGE TWO: Where does a woman get contraception?

- Select pictures of: a private room in a clinic with a nurse
  a pharmacy
  a general practice setting.

- Ask service users to match the pictures to the contraceptive and to the woman's body.

STAGE THREE: When does a woman use contraception?

- Select pictures of a bathroom, a bedroom and a clinic room.
- Ask service users to match the pictures to the contraceptive and to the woman's body.

Other things to do

- Use pictures of male and female bodies and ask who uses the different contraception and when, for example, when they are having sex, before or after. (You could develop characters for these people.)
- Where does the man get contraception? Match the pictures as before.

What shall we use?

> **Purpose:** to reinforce the need to discuss which contraceptive to use.
>
> **Previous knowledge:** understanding of private body parts.

How to do it:

- Use pictures of bodies clothed and unclothed.
- Develop the characters, for example, who they are, how old they are, their lives or jobs.
- When do they talk about contraception?
- Use situation cards – when is a good time?
- Turn over the cards one by one and agree when is a good time, for example, on the bus, in the pub, just as they start to have sex or in a private bedroom.
- What do they say?
- First line cards – place the cards into piles: good and bad ways to start the conversation
  "You are on the pill aren't you?"
  "Have you taken care of it?"
  "This is great. I really like you. Let's talk about how we can have sex safely."
  "I really want to have sex with you but I don't want a baby. Can we talk about it?"

No excuses!

> **Purpose:** how to negotiate using a condom.
>
> **Previous knowledge:** make sure the service users have done prior work about pressures to have sex – making choices and resisting unwanted approaches: you could use activities in *Talking together … about sex and relationships* for this.

How to do it:

- Present a range of pictures cut from magazines, such as men and women from different ages or backgrounds.
- Ask the student/s to match up people who may fancy each other focusing firstly on heterosexual relationships, using the female/male pictures.

- Ask the student/s which of the pairings would use a condom and why?

- You can also use this activity to consider homosexuality and safer sex. You can develop discussion about the types of relationships these people may have and why they like/fancy each other.

Speech cards

- First try to identify which of the negative cards could be a male voice, a female voice or belong to either sex. This could begin a discussion about who takes responsibility for contraception in the relationship and how this is seen by the couple and society in general.

- Match up a pair of pictures, one male and one female. Put the speech card next to the person identified as the speaker.

- Ask the student/s to choose from three options of positive speech cards to respond and place it beside the other character.

- Discuss whether this is a good answer and if it would work in a relationship.

- Using different pairings of pictures, repeat the activity with the range of positive and negative speech cards. This activity can be used to discuss safer sex within both heterosexual and homosexual relationships.

Negative speech cards

"I don't like condoms. They smell horrible."

"Don't expect me to touch your penis if you wear one of those."

"Don't ask me to put it on. I'll break it/put it on inside out."

"It's just not as sexy as skin to skin."

"I don't like fiddling around with the packet in the heat of the moment."

"A condom never fits me. It's too small/big/short."

"I won't be able to feel anything."

"It takes all the fun out of it."

"You have to stop and put a condom on right in the middle – it spoils the mood."

"It's up to the woman to think about contraception. She's the one who would get pregnant."

"I'm too shy."

"Don't you trust me?"

"They don't really work, you know."

"Don't bother – I'm on the pill."

"Do you think I've got an infection?"

Positive speech cards

"Most condoms don't smell of anything unless you'd like to try a strawberry one."

"I know how to put a condom on. Don't worry, I'm sure it won't break."

"That's fine. I'll do it."

"There will be plenty of chances for us to touch each other. It's only a bit of me that's got a condom on."

"I know how to open a condom packet quickly at the right moment so just relax."

"There's lots of different types of condoms. I'm sure we'll find one that fits you."

"An orgasm is still an orgasm when you wear a condom."

"It takes the risk out of it – I don't want to get pregnant or get an infection."

"I don't want to be with a man who can't take responsibility for sex."

"I am thinking about contraception. I'm on the pill. I'm also thinking about staying healthy – aren't you?"

"Don't worry. I feel shy too. We can giggle about it together."

"I would trust you more if you were responsible enough to use a condom."

"They work okay if you know how to use them – I'll show you."

"It's not just about getting pregnant. There are other reasons for using a condom, you know."

"Better safe than sorry. Let's keep us both healthy."

Other things you can do

● Ask students for excuses people might use.

● Ask them to 'beat my line' so read out the excuse and ask them to think of a good response, then tell them the one you have from the list above.

● Create two teams, one representing the man and one the woman. Place a chair in front of each team with the picture of the relevant character. In turn, one team (or their representative adult) reads out one of the excuses and the other team has to think of a reply. A different person should say the excuse and the reply each time so it does not become personal.

The condom moment

> **Purpose:** understanding when is a good time to negotiate using a condom.
>
> **Previous knowledge:** service users will need to have covered work about different types of relationships, the steps of developing a sexual relationship, and how to negotiate choices and decisions with relationships.

How to do it:

● Create two characters and find pictures to represent an evening out.

● The task is to work out when is the right moment to bring up the subject of condoms. You can use pictures to show situations and rooms where the characters are, for example:
  — at the pharmacy that afternoon
  — in the bus/taxi on the way to the pub
  — the pub
  — the club
  — in the taxi going home
  — by the front door
  — in the living room having coffee
  — on the stairs
  — in the bedroom, clothes on
  — in the bedroom, clothes off
  — just prior to penetration.

● Ask students to suggest what the characters might be thinking or saying at these different moments. Ask them when they think is the best time to bring up the subject of using condoms. Find the best way of negotiating condom use at these different times and emphasise the importance of talking about it before having sex.

More activities about condoms can be found in *Let's Do It* (see *Appendix One*).

Appendix One: Useful resources

This list only includes resources which are currently in print and available for purchase. There are, however, many good resources which are out of print. Copies may be available from libraries, or from health promotion units. Some are available from the website www.me-and-us.co.uk.

Publishers details are listed by the resource, unless they appear in the Useful organisations list on page 36.

Resources for young people with learning disabilities

All about us
FPA
A CD-ROM to help the personal development of people with learning disabilities around sex, sexuality and relationships. A self-study learning tool that can be used by someone with learning disabilities on their own or with support.

Books Beyond Words
A series of illustrated booklets with no words (or very few) designed to assist people with learning disabilities. Subject areas covered include health, emotions, abuse and lifestyle.
Available from:
Tel: 020 7235 2351 ext 146.
www.rcpsych.ac.uk

Everything You Ever Wanted to Know About Safer Sex ... but Nobody Bothered to Tell You
Nigel Bull with Camden People First
Information about safer sex and the prevention of HIV for people with learning disabilities.
Available from:
Tel: 020 7820 6655

Jason's Private World
Life support productions
DVD for men with learning disabilities.
Covers consent and saying no, safer sex and condoms.
Available from:
Tel: 020 7723 7520
www.lifesupportproductions.co.uk

Kylie's Private World
Life support productions
DVD for women with learning disabilities.
Covers periods, sanitary protection, consent, saying no and safer sex.
Available from:
Tel: 020 7723 7520
www.lifesupportproductions.co.uk

You, Your Body and Sex
Life support productions
Animated and interactive SRE DVD for people with learning disabilities.
Features all the content from *Jason's private world* and *Kylie's private world*.
Available from:
Tel: 020 7723 7520
www.lifesupportproductions.co.uk

The New Guide to Relationships and Sex
Life support productions
An SRE DVD for young people with mild learning disabilities.

Resources for people who work with young people with learning disabilities

FPA booklets
A wide range of sexual health booklets covering contraception, STIs and pregnancy choices. Regularly revised and updated. Available from:
FPA
Tel: 0845 122 8600
Email: fpadirect@fpa.org.uk
www.fpa.org.uk.

Contraceptive Display Kit
FPA
An ideal resource to use with young people when discussing contraception. The kit contains samples of contraceptives, a condom demonstrator, FPA booklets on contraception and a manual containing a variety of exercises. (The exercises are not written for work with young people with learning disabilities.)

Learning Disabilities, Sex and the Law. A Practical Guide
Claire Fanstone and Sarah Andrews
FPA
Reference book to help those who work with people with learning disabilities. Aims to answer common questions and provides information on the Sexual Offences Act 2003 and other relevant legislation in a clear, easy-to-read style.

Sexuality and Learning Disability: a Resource for Staff
Claire Fanstone and Zarine Katrak
FPA
Issues and dilemmas common to staff working with people with learning disabilities are discussed, together with practical tips, ideas on developing policy and awareness and a list of useful resources.

Talking Together … About Growing Up: a Workbook for Parents of Children with Learning Disabilities
Lorna Scott and Lesley Kerr Edwards
FPA
Essential resource to support parents to help their children who are approaching, or around the age of, puberty understand about growing up. The book covers the life cycle, body parts, public and private, keeping safe, feelings, growing up and looking ahead. It can also be used within the school setting or by schools working in partnership with parents.

Talking Together … About Sex and Relationships: a Practical Resource for Schools and Parents Working with Young People with Learning Disabilities
Lesley Kerr-Edwards and Lorna Scott
FPA
Following on from Talking Together … about growing up this book follows Tom and Debbie and their circle of friends at a particular point in their lives. Illustrated stories and activities for the classroom and home cover preparing to leave school and go to college, learning to keep safe, relationships, understanding sexuality and sexual behaviour, sexual choices and sexual health and future possibilities.

Confidentiality in Schools

Sheila White, Brook
For teachers, school nurses, school governors and other professionals working with young people. Discusses confidentiality in the context of PSHE education and provides ideas for workshop activities.
Available from:
www.brook.org.uk

Exploring Sexual and Social Understanding

British Institute of Learning Disabilities
178 line drawings showing mostly adults with a range of themes such as masturbation, heterosexual and homosexual relationships, abusive relationships and condom use.
Available from:
Tel: 0845 370 0067
www.bild.org.uk

Faith, Values and Sex and Relationships Education (Forum factsheet)

NCB Publications
Factsheet looking at the issues involved in developing an approach to SRE which is inclusive of diverse faith perspectives.
Available from:
www.ncb.org.uk/sef

Growing and Learning about Sexual Heath

Jane Keeling
Three packs of exercises, games and activities for young people with learning disabilities and autism. One for young people, one for young women and one for young men.
Available from:
www.growingandlearning.co.uk

Holding On, Letting Go. Sex, Sexuality and People with Learning Disabilities

John Drury, Lynne Hutchinson and Jon Wright, Souvenir Press
Book for parents and carers of people with a learning disability to help them feel more confident when thinking about sexuality in relation to their son or daughter.
Available from:
Bookpoint Tel: 01235 400400

Let's Do It: Creative Activities for Sex Education for Young People with Learning Disabilities

R Johns, L Scott and J Bliss, Image in Action
Activities using visual images and drama for use in schools, colleges and day centres.
Available from:
Tel: 01494 481632
www.imageinaction.org

Let's Plan It: a Guide to Planning Programmes of Sex Education for Young People and Adults with Learning Disabilities

L Scott and S Duignan, Image in Action
How to plan programmes for a wide range of groups including weekly session sheets and new Image in Action activities.
Available from:
Tel: 01494 481632
www.imageinaction.org

Living Your Life

A Craft, re-edited S Bustard, Brook
Sex and relationships education resource, divided into eight modules. Contraception is covered in module seven.
Available from:
www.brook.org.uk

Male and Female Cloth Models

BodySense
Anatomically correct, half life-size clothed models, with detailed notes.
Available from:
Tel: 01905 840266.
www.bodysense.org.uk

Model of Female Genitalia

BodySense
Anatomically correct 3D model of female genitalia and reproductive organs.
Available from:
Tel: 01905 840266.
www.bodysense.org.uk

Picture Yourself

Hilary Dixon, illustrations David Gifford
Me-and-Us Ltd.
Four sets of 48 line drawings and
photographs with educators' notes
on CD. Themes include Growing up;
In public and private; Making
relationships; Being private.
Available from:
Tel: 01539 621 777
www.me-and-us.co.uk

Picture Yourself 2: Social and Sex Education for People with Learning Disabilities

Hilary Dixon, illustrations David Gifford.
Me-and-Us Ltd.
193 picture cards with educators'
notes on CD. Themes include Me as
an individual; Relationships with others;
Menstruation and wet dreams;
Sexual health; Pregnancy, birth and
parenthood; Single sex relationships.
Available from:
Tel: 01539 621 777
www.me-and-us.co.uk

Sex and Relationships Education for Children and Young People with Learning Difficulties

Sex Education Forum
Factsheet supporting staff in special
schools, mainstream schools and
other settings in developing and
reviewing SRE policy.
Available from:
www.ncb.org.uk/sef

Sex and Relationship Education for Children with Learning Disabilities or Disabilities: Resource List

Sex Education Forum
Factsheet providing information on
resources including books, videos
and websites.
Available from:
www.ncb.org.uk/sef

Sex and the Three Rs – Rights, Responsibilities and Risks

Michelle McCarthy and David Thompson,
Pavilion
An SRE package for working with
people with learning difficulties.
Available from:
Tel: 0844 880 5061
www.pavpub.com

Young Disabled People Can

Brook
Range of leaflets and posters showing
positive images of young disabled people.
Available from:
www.brook.org.uk

Appendix Two:
Useful organisations

How FPA can help you
sexual health direct is a nationwide
service run by FPA. It provides:

- confidential information and advice
  and a wide range of booklets on
  individual methods of contraception,
  common sexually transmitted
  infections, pregnancy choices,
  abortion and planning a pregnancy

- details of contraception, sexual
  health and genitourinary medicine
  (GUM) clinics and sexual assault
  referral centres.

FPA helplines

England
helpline 0845 122 8690
9am to 6pm Monday to Friday

Northern Ireland
helpline 0845 122 8687
9am to 5pm Monday to Friday

or visit the FPA website **www.fpa.org.uk**

To order FPA publications contact:
FPA
Tel: 0845 122 8600
Fax: 0845 123 2349
Email: fpadirect@fpa.org.uk
www.fpa.org.uk

British Institute of Learning
Disabilities
Tel: 01562 723010
www.bild.org.uk
Information, publications, training
and consultancy services.

Brook
Tel: 020 7284 6040
Helpline: 0808 802 1234
www.brook.org.uk
Runs local young people's sexual health
services. Produces a range of sexual
health resources for young people and
those who work with them.

Enable
Tel: 0141 226 4541
www.enable.org.uk
Membership organisation for people
with learning disabilities and their family
carers in Scotland.

Health and Social Care in
Northern Ireland
www.n-i.nhs.uk
Health information for people in Northern
Ireland.

Health of Wales Information Service
Tel: 0845 46 47
www.wales.nhs.uk
Health information for people in Wales.

Image in Action
Tel: 01494 481632
www.imageinaction.org
Works with groups of young people and
adults in schools, colleges and centres,
publishes resources and provides
training and a consultancy service for
organisations providing SRE for people
with learning disabilities.

Mencap
Helpline: 0808 808 1111
www.mencap.org.uk
Works with people with a learning
disability, their families and carers. Has a
network of affiliated groups throughout
England, Northern Ireland and Wales.

National Youth Agency
Tel: 0116 242 7350
www.nya.org.uk
Produces resources about sex and
relationships for the mainstream
youth centre setting.

NHS Choices
www.nhs.uk
Information on conditions, treatments,
local services and healthy living.

NHS Direct
Tel: 0845 46 47
www.nhs.uk
Health information for people in England.

NHS Scotland
Tel: NHS 24 on 08454 24 24 24
www.show.scot.nhs.uk
Health information for people in Scotland.

People First
Tel: 020 7820 6655
www.peoplefirstltd.com
www.peoplefirst.org.uk (easy read)
Organisation run by and for people
with learning disabilities. Has a library
and produces information, a newsletter
and resources.

Respond
Tel: 0808 808 0700
www.respond.org.uk
Confidential helpline for people
with learning disabilities who have
experienced abuse.

Sex Education Forum
Tel: 020 7843 6000
www.ncb.org.uk/sef
Advice and publications on developing
sex and relationships policies,
working with parents and carers and
good practice in delivering SRE.

Sexwise
Tel: 0800 28 29 30
Confidential information and advice
for young people, including details of
local services.

Appendix Three:
Where can I get help?

Where to go for advice on sex and relationships

The proforma on the following page is intended for local use. You can photocopy and complete it with information about your local area, or use it as a starting point to develop your own materials. Include details of local contraception and sexual health clinics, services for young people and helplines. Add some photographs of local places. Use it with groups of service users or give it to individuals to use. A visit to a local clinic is a good way to make the information come alive.

Where can I get help?

Where to go for advice on sex and relationships

Where can I get help about contraception?

Where can I get help with sexually transmitted infections (STIs)?

Where can I get condoms?

How do I get to a clinic(s)?

Can I bring a friend or supporter?

Where to go for advice on sex and relationships:

Address: _____

_____

Tel: _____

Bus: _____

Clinic times: _____